S0-BCP-269

The Three Little Pigs Houses

Oink, Oink, Oink

Senior Authors

J. David Cooper
John J. Pikulski

Authors

Kathryn H. Au
Margarita Calderón
Jacqueline C. Comas
Marjorie Y. Lipson
J. Sabrina Mims
Susan E. Page
Sheila W. Valencia
MaryEllen Vogt

Consultants

Dolores Malcolm
Tina Saldivar
Shane Templeton

Acknowledgments appear on page Acknowledgments 1 at the back of this book.

Printed in the U.S.A.   ISBN: 0-395-79514-1   23456789-WC-98 97

INVITATIONS TO LITERACY

Houghton Mifflin Company • Boston

Atlanta • Dallas • Geneva, Illinois • Palo Alto • Princeton

The kids in Room 207 were misbehaving again. Spitballs stuck to the ceiling. Paper planes whizzed through the air. They were the worst-behaved class in the whole school.

"Now settle down," said Miss Nelson in a sweet voice.

But the class would *not* settle down. They whispered and giggled. They squirmed and made faces. They were even rude during story hour. And they always refused to do their lessons.

"Something will have to be done," said Miss Nelson.

The next morning Miss Nelson did not come to school. "Wow!" yelled the kids. "Now we can *really* act up!" They began to make more spitballs and paper planes. "Today let's be just terrible!" they said.

"Not so fast!" hissed an unpleasant voice.

A woman in an ugly black dress stood before them. "I am your new teacher, Miss Viola Swamp." And she rapped the desk with her ruler.

"Where is Miss Nelson?" asked the kids.

"Never mind that!" snapped Miss Swamp. "Open those arithmetic books!" Miss Nelson's kids did as they were told.

They could see that Miss Swamp was a real witch.
She meant business.

Right away she put them to work. And she loaded
them down with homework.

"We'll have no story hour today," said Miss Swamp.

"Keep your mouths shut," said Miss Swamp.

"Sit perfectly still," said Miss Swamp.

"And if you misbehave, you'll be sorry," said Miss Swamp.

The kids in Room 207 had *never* worked so hard.

Days went by and there was no sign of Miss Nelson. The kids *missed* Miss Nelson!

"Maybe we should try to find her," they said.
Some of them went to the police.

Detective McSmogg was assigned to the case.
He listened to their story. He scratched his chin.
"Hmmmm," he said. "Hmmm. I think Miss Nelson is
missing."

Detective McSmogg would not be much help.

Other kids went to Miss Nelson's house. The shades were tightly drawn, and no one answered the door. In fact, the only person they *did* see was the wicked Miss Viola Swamp, coming up the street.

"If she sees us, she'll give us more homework." They got away just in time.

Maybe something *terrible* happened to Miss
Nelson! "Maybe she was gobbled up by a shark!" said
one of the kids. But that didn't seem likely.

"Maybe Miss Nelson went to Mars!" said another
kid. But that didn't seem likely either.

"I know!" exclaimed one know-it-all. "Maybe Miss Nelson's car was carried off by a swarm of angry butterflies!" But that was the least likely of all.

The kids in Room 207 became very discouraged. It seemed that Miss Nelson was never coming back. And they would be stuck with Miss Viola Swamp forever.

They heard footsteps in the hall. "Here comes the witch," they whispered.

"Hello, children," someone said in a sweet voice.

It was Miss Nelson! "Did you miss me?" she asked.

"We certainly did!" cried all the kids. "Where were you?"

"That's my little secret," said Miss Nelson. "How about a story hour?"

"Oh, yes!" cried the kids.

Miss Nelson noticed that during story hour no one was rude or silly. "What brought about this lovely change?" she asked.

"That's *our* little secret," said the kids.

Back home Miss Nelson took off her coat and
hung it in the closet (right next to an ugly black dress).
When it was time for bed she sang a little song.
"I'll never tell," she said to herself with a smile.

P. S. Detective McSmogg is working on a new case.
He is *now* looking for Miss Viola Swamp.

Meet the Author
Harry Allard

Harry Allard is always writing
something. He keeps a diary.
He writes a lot of letters. And,
of course, he writes books.
When Allard gets an idea for a
story, he just begins writing.
Even if it's three in the morning.

Meet the Illustrator
James Marshall

How would you like to have Miss
Viola Swamp for a teacher?
James Marshall once said that
he had a second grade teacher
like her. In fact, when he drew
Miss Swamp, he kept his
teacher in mind.

Harry Allard and James Marshall were a team for
almost twenty years. Two other popular books by
them are The Stupids Step Out and Miss Nelson
Is Back.

Investigating the Story

Put On a Puppet Show

Settle Down, Class!

What might Miss Nelson and Miss Swamp say to *your* class? Make puppets of them. Then, with a partner, make up things for them to say.

Make a Poster

Wanted: Miss Viola Swamp

Help Detective McSmogg find Miss Viola Swamp. Create a "Wanted" poster. Be sure to include a picture of her and a description of the way she acts.

29

Oink, Oink, Oink

e Three Lit

STRAW HOUSE
SCALE: 3/16" = 1'-0"

The Pigs' Houses

31

Oink, Oink, Oink **Contents**

Oink, Oink, Oink Read On Your Own

PAPERBACK PLUS

Sidney Rella and the Glass Sneaker

by Bernice Myers

When Sidney wants to be a football star, his fairy godfather helps out.

In the same book . . .

The original "Cinderella," plus a photo guessing game to keep you on your toes.

Sleeping Ugly

by Jane Yolen

Plain Jane's no beauty. Will the prince awaken her?

In the same book . . .
The unfractured version, plus some tired old jokes.

Books to Squeal About

All Pigs Are Beautiful
by Dick King-Smith
This author loves pigs. For the first time, he tells why.

The Great Pig Escape
by Eileen Christelow
When Bert's pigs hear they're bound to be bacon, they make a break for it.

The True Story of the 3 Little Pigs
by Jon Scieszka
The wolf finally gets to tell *his* side of the story.

The Fourth Little Pig
by Teresa Celsi
Bet you didn't know the three little pigs had a sister.

The Three Little Pigs and the Fox
by William H. Hooks
It's suppertime, and this fox wants pork chops.

About the Author

Eugene Trivizas has written many books — but in Greek. *The Three Little Wolves and the Big Bad Pig* is the first book he wrote in English. Eugene lives part of the year in Greece and part of the year in England. He has written about many subjects, including football and crime.

About the Illustrator

Helen Oxenbury has always loved to draw and paint. She once had a job drawing pictures for birthday cards and other greeting cards you buy in stores. Now she lives with her family in London, England, and illustrates books for children.

Once upon a time, there were three cuddly little
wolves with soft fur and fluffy tails who lived
with their mother. The first was black, the
second was gray, and the third was white.

One day the mother called the three little wolves
around her and said, "My children, it is time for you to
go out into the world. Go and build a house for
yourselves. But beware of the big bad pig."

"Don't worry, Mother, we will watch out for him,"
said the three little wolves, and they set off.

Soon they met a kangaroo who was pushing a wheelbarrow full of red and yellow bricks.

"Please, will you give us some of your bricks?" asked the three little wolves.

"Certainly," said the kangaroo, and she gave them lots of red and yellow bricks.

So the three little wolves built themselves a house of bricks.

The very next day the big bad pig came prowling down the road and saw the house of bricks that the little wolves had built.

The three little wolves were playing croquet in the garden. When they saw the big bad pig coming, they ran inside the house and locked the door.

The pig knocked on the door and grunted, "Little wolves, little wolves, let me come in!"

"No, no, no," said the three little wolves. "By the hair on our chinny-chin-chins, we will not let you in, not for all the tea leaves in our china teapot!"

"Then I'll huff and I'll puff and I'll blow your house down!" said the pig.

So he huffed and he puffed and he puffed and he huffed, but the house didn't fall down.

But the pig wasn't called big and bad for
nothing. He went and fetched his sledgehammer,
and he knocked the house down.

The three little wolves only just managed to
escape before the bricks crumbled, and they were
very frightened indeed.

"We shall have to build a stronger house,"
they said.

Just then they saw a beaver who was mixing
concrete in a concrete mixer.

"Please, will you give us some of your concrete?"
asked the three little wolves.

"Certainly," said the beaver, and he gave them buckets and buckets full of messy, slurry concrete.

So the three little wolves built themselves a house of concrete.

No sooner had they finished than the big bad pig came prowling down the road and saw the house of concrete that the little wolves had built.

They were playing battledore and shuttlecock in the garden, and when they saw the big bad pig coming, they ran inside their house and shut the door.

The pig rang the bell and said, "Little frightened wolves, let me come in!"

"No, no, no," said the three little wolves. "By the hair on our chinny-chin-chins, we will not let you in, not for all the tea leaves in our china teapot."

"Then I'll huff and I'll puff and I'll blow your house down!" said the pig.

So he huffed and he puffed and he puffed and he huffed, but the house didn't fall down.

47

But the pig wasn't called big and bad for nothing. He went and fetched his pneumatic drill and smashed the house down.

The three little wolves managed to escape, but their chinny-chin-chins were trembling and trembling and trembling.

"We shall build an even stronger house," they said, because they were very determined. Just then they saw a truck coming along the road carrying barbed wire, iron bars, armor plates, and heavy metal padlocks.

"Please, will you give us some of your barbed wire, a few iron bars and armor plates, and some heavy metal padlocks?" they said to the rhinoceros who was driving the truck.

"Sure," said the rhinoceros, and he gave them plenty of barbed wire, iron bars, armor plates, and heavy metal padlocks. He also gave them some Plexiglas and some reinforced steel chains, because he was a generous and kind-hearted rhinoceros.

So the three little wolves built themselves an extremely strong house. It was the strongest, securest house one could possibly imagine. They felt absolutely safe.

The next day the big bad pig came prowling along the road as usual. The three little wolves were playing hopscotch in the garden. When they saw the big bad pig coming, they ran inside their house, bolted the door, and locked all the thirty-seven padlocks.

The pig dialed the video entrance phone and said, "Little frightened wolves with the trembling chins, let me come in!"

"No, no, no!" said the little wolves. "By the hair on our chinny-chin-chins, we will not let you in, not for all the tea leaves in our china teapot."

"Then I'll huff and I'll puff and I'll blow your house down!" said the pig.

So he huffed and he puffed and he puffed and he huffed, but the house didn't fall down.

But the pig wasn't called big and bad for nothing. He rented a crane, drove it to the house, swung the wrecking ball as high as it could go, and . . .

51

he demolished the house. The three little wolves just managed to escape with their fluffy tails flattened.

"Something must be wrong with our building materials," they said. "We have to try something different. But *what?*"

At that moment they saw a flamingo coming along pushing a wheelbarrow full of flowers.

"Please, will you give us some flowers?" asked the little wolves.

"With pleasure," said the flamingo, and he gave them lots of flowers. So the three little wolves built themselves a house of flowers.

53

One wall was of marigolds, one of daffodils, one of pink roses, and one of cherry blossoms. The ceiling was made of sunflowers, and the floor was a carpet of daisies. They had water lilies in their bathtub, and buttercups in their refrigerator. It was a rather fragile house and it swayed in the wind, but it was very beautiful.

Next day the big bad pig came prowling down the road and saw the house of flowers that the three little wolves had built.

He rang the bluebell at the door and said, "Little frightened wolves with the trembling chins and the flattened tails, let me come in!"

"No, no, no," said the three little wolves. "By the hair on our chinny-chin-chins, we will not let you in, not for all the tea leaves in our china teapot!"

"Then I'll huff and I'll puff and I'll blow your house down!" said the pig.

But as he took a deep breath, ready to huff and
puff, he smelled the soft scent of the flowers. It was
fantastic. And because the scent was so lovely, the pig
took another breath and then another. Instead of
huffing and puffing, he began to sniff.

He sniffed deeper and deeper until he was quite
filled with the fragrant scent. His heart grew tender,
and he realized how horrible he had been. Right then
he decided to become a big *good* pig.

He started to sing and to dance the tarantella.

At first the three little wolves were a bit worried. It might be a trick. But soon they realized that the pig had truly changed, so they came running out of the house.

They started playing games with him.

First they played pig-pog and then piggy-in-the-middle, and when they were all tired, they invited him into the house.

They offered him tea and strawberries and wolfberries, and asked him to stay with them as long as he wanted.

The pig accepted, and they all lived happily together ever after.

Building on the Story

Design a House

Home, Sweet Home

What else other than flowers could turn a big bad pig into a big *good* pig? With a partner, design a new house made out of something that looks, smells, or tastes really good.

Tell a Story

Twice Upon a Time

Think of another story you can turn inside out. Maybe the Three Bears pay a visit to Goldilocks' house or Little Red Riding Hood dresses like the wolf's granny.

Eight-week-old gray wolf pups are usually busy little creatures. Luckily, this one is sitting still long enough for us to get a good look. Gretta is her name, and she's taking a break after a morning romp. She won't rest for long, though. What's next? Turn the page to see what kind of mischief she might stir up.

What's UP, Pup?

by Lyle Prescott
photos by Art Wolfe

Ranger Rick

Chomp! "OK, grass — you haven't got a chance against a tough wolf like me," Gretta might be thinking (**right**). Like other young wolf pups, she likes to play with and explore almost everything around her. (She may even eat the grass after she finishes "attacking" it.)

Gretta is also practicing using her teeth. See those pointy ones at the sides of her mouth? They're called *canines* (KAY-nines), and they'll help her hunt when she gets older.

Every day, wolf pups tumble and wrestle together (**left**). Playing like this helps the pups figure out which ones will later be bosses and which ones will get bossed around. Plus, the fast-growing pups need to exercise their muscles. By the time autumn comes, they'll have to be strong enough to join the adults at hunting time.

The other frisky wolf pups have dashed off without Gretta. They couldn't have gone far — but where are they? She throws back her head and lets out a long, sad howl (**right**). "Hey, guys, you left me here all alone — *please* come back," the little pup seems to be calling.

A wolf may howl alone, or a pack may howl together in a chorus. Either way, the sounds can carry for a long distance. Sometimes wolves may howl messages to each other from a mile or two apart.

The wolf pups like to hang out all over Mom (**above**). That's Gretta in front, giving Mom a lick. Luckily for the little pups, the adult wolves are never too old to play. 🐾

It oinks! It wallows! It hangs out with the litter! Here's all the dirt on . . .

This Little Piggy!

by Linda Granfield

Can pigs swim?

What good are pigs' snouts?

Are pigs smart?

Are all pigs born with curly tails?

Do pigs prefer to be dirty?

Do pigs really make pigs of themselves?

Go hog wild. Take a look at these questions and see how many you can answer. If you think pigs are hard to peg down, you're right!

Pigs swim on hot, sunny days.

You might be surprised to know that pigs are great dog paddlers! Sometimes, they'll escape the burning sun by taking a swim at a water hole. The large amount of fat in their bodies helps keep even heavy pigs floating in the water. Pigs are such good swimmers they can cross rivers many kilometers (miles) wide.

A pig's snout is a pig's best friend.

Sure, a pig's snout is used for breathing — but it's also great for sweating, digging, and reaching out to other pigs! Like a dog, a pig sweats through its nose instead of its skin. A pig counts on its snout's flat front and bony upper rim as it digs in the dirt and unearths tasty roots. But all that digging doesn't harden a pig's nose. It remains moist and tender — perfect for greeting another pig snout-to-snout when they meet!

When Pigs Fly

Pigs have trotted their way into many of our expressions. See if you can match each of these with its meaning. Then check your answers on page 66.

1. pigpen   a. stubborn

2. pig-headed   b. braid

3. go whole hog   c. living well

4. pigtail   d. never

5. high off the hog e. messy place

6. when pigs fly   f. take to the limit

GREAT ATTRACTION !
WONDER and ADMIRATION of the
WORLD !
THE LEARNED
NOVELTY &   AMUSEMENT!
PIG !
Mr JAMES L. HAZARD,
Respectfully informs the Ladies and Gentlemen of this place and vicinity, that the fol-
lowing performance of this
NOW, OR   NEVER !
EXTRAORDINARY PIG

Pigs are smarter than you think!

Pigs were one of the first animals to be trained by people. In 1785, a famous hog, called the Learned Pig, was taught to spell words, tell time, and solve math problems with the help of rewards. Today, some scientists believe that pigs are very intelligent and easier to train than dogs. They report that pigs can easily find their way through mazes that prove too difficult for many other animals.

Straight or curly pig tails tell tales.

Many, but not all, breeds of pigs are born with curly tails. But when a kinky-tailed pig is scared or not feeling well, its tail may straighten out. Do all curly pig tails curl in the same direction? One old American saying claims that pigs' tails in the south twist clockwise, while pigs' tails in the north twist the opposite way.

Pigs won't stuff themselves silly.

Pigs will eat almost anything — even snow! But that doesn't mean pigs go hog wild over food. Unlike cows and horses, which will eat until they are ill, pigs stop when they feel full. After they have eaten, they usually nap until the next meal. Even without snacking between breakfast and dinner, pigs grow very quickly!

Answers to "When Pigs Fly":   1. e   2. a   3. f   4. b   5. c   6. d

Picks of the Litter

Whether you're in Africa or Asia or somewhere in South America, you'll find a wild pig cousin or two! The **bush pig (a)** lives in the grasslands of Africa and Madagascar. Like a wart hog (another African wild pig), male bush pigs have warts on their faces. These warts help protect their faces from the tusks of other bush pigs when they fight. The **babirusa (b)** makes its home in southeast Asia. Its teeth, which can be longer than your foot, grow through the roof of its mouth and out the top of its snout. The **collared peccary (c)**, from South and Central America, is a more distant pig relation. A peccary will "woof" like a dog when its enemy the jaguar is nearby.

Pigs look dirty but really they're cool.

If you visit a farm, you'll probably find pigs covered with dried, caked mud. But it's not because pigs want to be dirty. They need the moisture found in mud. Pigs are very sensitive to heat but have no sweat glands to help them cool off. A coating of mud lowers their body temperature and stops sunburn. If there's clean water nearby, pigs will use that, too.

67

MEET THE AUTHOR

SUSAN LOWELL has some wild neighbors who often come over for a cactus dinner. That's because she lives in the Arizona desert, and her neighbors are piglike animals called *javelinas* (ha-ve-LEE-nas). The javelinas like to eat the thorny stems of the cactuses that grow near her ranch. Lowell enjoys watching the javelinas so much that she made up a story about them.

MEET THE ILLUSTRATOR

JIM HARRIS lives in Colorado on the side of a flat-topped mountain called a *mesa*. Every night, he can hear coyotes howling outside. Sometimes he even sees an elk walk across the deck outside his art studio. Harris has been drawing and painting since he was four years old.

68

THE THREE LITTLE JAVELINAS

by Susan Lowell
Illustrated by Jim Harris

ONCE UPON A TIME,

way out in the desert, there were three little javelinas. Javelinas (ha-ve-LEE-nas) are wild, hairy, southwestern cousins of pigs.

Their heads were hairy, their backs were hairy, and their bony legs — all the way down to their hard little hooves — were very hairy. But their snouts were soft and pink.

One day, the three little javelinas trotted away to seek their fortunes. In this hot, dry land, the sky was almost always blue. Steep purple mountains looked down on the desert, where the cactus forests grew.

Soon the little javelinas came to a spot where the path divided, and each one went a different way.

The first little javelina wandered lazily along. He didn't see a dust storm whirling across the desert — until it caught him.

The whirlwind blew away and left the first little javelina sitting in a heap of tumbleweeds. Brushing himself off, he said, "I'll build a house with them!" And in no time at all, he did.

Then along came a coyote. He ran through the desert so quickly and so quietly that he was almost invisible. In fact, this was only one of Coyote's many magical tricks. He laughed when he saw the tumbleweed house and smelled the javelina inside.

"Mmm! A tender juicy piggy!" he thought. Coyote was tired of eating mice and rabbits.

He called out sweetly, "Little pig, little pig, let me come in."

"Not by the hair of my chinny-chin-chin!" shouted the first javelina (who had a lot of hair on his chinny-chin-chin!).

"Then I'll huff, and I'll puff, and I'll blow your house in!" said Coyote.

And he huffed, and he puffed, and he blew the little tumbleweed house away.

But in all the hullabaloo, the first little javelina escaped — and went looking for his brother and sister.

Coyote, who was very sneaky, tiptoed along behind.

The second little javelina walked for miles among giant cactus plants called saguaros (sa-WA-ros). They held their ripe red fruit high in the sky. But they made almost no shade, and the little javelina grew hot.

Then he came upon a Native American woman who was gathering sticks from inside a dried-up cactus. She planned to use these long sticks, called saguaro ribs, to knock down the sweet cactus fruit.

The second little javelina said, "Please, may I have some sticks to build a house?"

"Ha'u," (how) she said, which means "yes" in the language of the Desert People.

When he was finished building his house, he lay down in the shade. Then his brother arrived, panting from the heat, and the second little javelina moved over and made a place for him.

Pretty soon, Coyote found the saguaro rib house. He used his magic to make his voice sound just like another javelina's.

"Little pig, little pig, let me come in!" he called.

But the little javelinas were suspicious. The second one cried, "No! Not by the hair of my chinny-chin-chin!"

"Bah!" thought Coyote. "I am not going to eat your *hair.*"

Then Coyote smiled, showing all his sharp teeth: "I'll huff, and I'll puff, and I'll blow your house in!"

So he huffed, and he puffed, and all the saguaro ribs came tumbling down.

But the two little javelinas escaped into the desert.

Still not discouraged, Coyote followed. Sometimes his magic did fail, but then he usually came up with another trick.

The third little javelina trotted
through beautiful palo verde trees,
with green trunks and yellow flowers.
She saw a snake sliding by, smooth as oil.
A hawk floated round and round above
her. Then she came to a place where a
man was making adobe (a-DOE-be) bricks
from mud and straw. The bricks lay on
the ground, baking in the hot sun.

The third little javelina thought for a moment,
and said, "May I please have a few adobes to build a
house?"

"*Sí,*" answered the man, which means "yes" in
Spanish, the brick-maker's language.

So the third javelina built herself a solid little
adobe house, cool in summer and warm in winter.
When her brothers found her, she welcomed them
in and locked the door behind them.

Coyote followed their trail.

"Little pig, little pig, let me come in!" he called.
The three little javelinas looked out the window. This time Coyote pretended to be very old and weak, with no teeth and a sore paw. But they were not fooled.

"No! Not by the hair of my chinny-chin-chin," called back the third little javelina.

"Then I'll huff, and I'll puff, and I'll blow your house in!" said Coyote. He grinned, thinking of the wild pig dinner to come.

"Just try it!" shouted the third little javelina. So Coyote huffed and puffed, but the adobe bricks did not budge.

Again, Coyote tried. "I'll HUFF ... AND I'LL PUFF ... AND I'LL BLOW YOUR HOUSE IN!"

The three little javelinas covered their hairy
ears. But nothing happened. The javelinas peeked
out the window.

The tip of Coyote's raggedy tail whisked right past their noses. He was climbing upon the tin roof. Next, Coyote used his magic to make himself very skinny.

"The stove pipe!" gasped the third little javelina. Quickly she lighted a fire inside her wood stove.

"What a feast it will be!" Coyote said to himself. He squeezed into the stove pipe. "I think I'll eat them with red hot chile sauce!"

Whoosh. S-s-sizzle!

Then the three little javelinas heard an amazing noise. It was not a bark. It was not a cackle. It was not a howl. It was not a scream. It was all of those sounds together.

"Yip

     yap

      yeep

       YEE-OWW-OOOOOOOOOOOOO!"

Away ran a puff of smoke shaped like a coyote.

The three little javelinas lived happily ever after in the adobe house.

And if you ever hear a Coyote's voice, way out in the desert at night . . . well, you know what he's remembering!

Something to Howl About

Write a Tale

Ah—roooooo!

Whenever Coyote remembers burning his tail, he howls at the moon. Write a story that explains the sound another animal makes. For example, tell why pigs oink or frogs croak.

Be a Songwriter

Showtime!

With a partner, make up a song about the three little javelinas. Use a tune you know, such as "Old MacDonald." Perform the song for your class.

My Hairy Neighbors

by Susan Lowell

photos by
Thomas A. Wiewandt

Meet some piglike animals that "talk" with stinky smells!

Welcome to my ranch. I live deep in a rocky canyon way out in the Arizona desert. I have many wild neighbors. At the end of a summer day, three of my favorites often come for dinner. Just watch!

There — a hairy animal is peeking through the bushes. And another. And another. It's Juan, José, and Josefina!

The animals are each about 20 inches (50 cm) high, with rounded backs. And they look and act a bit like pigs. But they're *peccaries* (PECK-a-rees). Some people around here also call them *javelinas* (ha-ve-LEE-nas).

Check out the rings of light hair around the necks of these peccaries. They look like collars, don't they? That's why the animals are called *collared peccaries*.

A peccary can use its long, sharp teeth to bite a prickly pear cactus. Those teeth may look nasty, but this animal is probably just yawning.

Peccaries live in groups called *herds*, which helps them protect each other from their enemies. And when it's snooze time, the herd snuggles close together.

Peccaries often kneel to dig for food. See this one's knees? It has thick pads of skin there from kneeling so much!

◄ A drippy hole on the javelina's back oozes a smelly liquid called *musk*. Family members rub the musk on each other. That helps them keep track of each other.

▲

Peccary herds stick close together. This young one found a safe place in its herd — right in the thick of things.

Peccaries don't live just in deserts. In Mexico and much of South America, they also can be found in mountains and rain forests. They live only in wild areas. But some of those wild areas are very close to the homes of people.

As I go into my house, I suddenly hear some loud noise. *Clang! Bang! Clatter!*

What's that? Uh-oh! Outside my ranch house, Josefina just knocked over one of the trash cans. Her babies poke their snouts inside it and sniff for something good to eat.

"Shoo!" I say. "No junk food! Go find some nice cactus fruit." Josefina grunts. Together the herd starts moving. "Good night!" I call to them. Then I watch the herd gallop off into the desert darkness.

About the Author

Donivee Martin Laird

The beautiful state of Hawaii is home to Donivee Martin Laird. She was born there and lives there today with her family and a mongoose named Custard. Laird has written several Hawaiian versions of popular tales, such as *Wili Wai Kula and the Three Mongooses*, a Hawaiian "Goldilocks and the Three Bears."

About the Illustrator

Don Stuart

Don Stuart didn't have any brothers or sisters growing up, so he used to entertain himself by drawing. Making his own comic books was a favorite thing to do. Among the illustrators Stuart admires today is Lane Smith, the illustrator of *The True Story of the 3 Little Pigs*.

The Three Little Hawaiian Pigs
and the
Magic Shark

One morning in Hawaii a mother and father pig
called their children together.

"Our dear pua'a keikis," they said with sorrow in
their voices. "As much as we love you, it is time for you
to become grown-ups and seek your own way in the

pua'a (poo AH ah) a Hawaiian word meaning pig

keiki (kay EE kee) what Hawaiians call a child

aloha (ah LOH ha) a Hawaiian word with meanings such as hello, goodbye, and love

world. Here is a sack of money for each of you. Spend it wisely and always be careful of strangers."

After saying aloha to their parents, the three little pigs set off down the road looking forward to a life full of happiness, adventure, and riches.

95

pili (PEE lee) **grass** a grass used to thatch grass houses in old Hawaii

opihi (oh PEE hee) a shallow, cone-shaped limpet shell whose animal is prized eating

They had gone only a short distance when they met a man with a load of pili grass. "Ah ha," said the first little pig. "This is for me. I will build myself a grass house and live beside the sea."

So, he bought the pili grass and happily headed towards the beach where he built his house. It was finished quickly and he took his pole, his net, his small bucket for opihi, and he went fishing.

96

The other two little pigs went on until they met a
man selling driftwood. "Ah ha," said the second little
pig. "This is for me. I will build myself a house of
driftwood and live beside the sea."

Feeling pleased with himself, he quickly built his
house and went to join the first little pig fishing and
scraping opihi off the slippery rocks.

lava rock formed by a volcano

pau (POW) finished, all done

The third little pig went on until he met a man selling lava rock. "Ah ha," said the third little pig. "This is for me. I will build myself a house of lava rock and live beside the sea and go fishing with my brothers."

It took many days to build the house and before it was done, one brother came to visit the third little pig.

"Why are you wasting your time on such a hard house to build?" he asked. "We are pau with our houses and have time to fish and take it easy surfing and playing. Forget this house, come with us."

The third little pig just shook his head and said he would rather take his time and build a strong house.

After many days of hard work, the lava rock house was finished. It was sturdy and strong and the third little pig was pleased with his work. He checked his doors and windows carefully to be sure his house was snug and safe.

Then off he went to join his brothers beside the sea.

yellow tang a small bright yellow reef fish

humuhumu (hoo moo HOO moo) a member of the trigger fish family; one of whom is the humuhumu-nukunuku-a-pua'a or fish with a snout like a pig, made famous in a popular Hawaiian song

he'e (HAY ay) the Hawaiian word for octopus

puhi paka (POOK hee PAH kah) a ferocious eel with sharp teeth

The three little pigs threw their nets and pulled in reef creatures like the brilliant yellow tang, the horned humuhumu, or the slimy octopus, he'e. They climbed over the wet rocks scraping off the delicious opihi and once in a while they caught puhi paka, the fierce fanged eel.

100

ulua (oo LOO ah) a kind of crevalle or jack fish

opakapaka (oh pah kah PAH kah) a blue snapper fish

ahi (AH hee) a yellow fin tuna fish

trade winds breezes which keep Hawaii cool

Sometimes they took their poles, and standing far out on the rocks, fished the deeper waters for the larger ulua, opakapaka, and ahi. They played tag, splashed in the tide pools, and chased tiny sand crabs. Their days were clear and sunny, and cooled by gentle trade winds.

101

When the waves broke just right beside the reef, they took their surfboards and caught long breathtaking rides to the beach.

Meanwhile, an evil magic shark watched them from deep down where the water is green. Back and forth swam the magic shark, his long teeth shining in the gloomy water. He especially wanted to eat the three little pigs since they looked so sweet and tender.

He knew he couldn't catch them on the rocks, for the lava was sharp and the pigs too quick. He wished they would fall off their surfboards, but the pigs were too good and went too fast through the rough water.

So, watching and planning, the magic shark drooled and thought of the yummy little pigs.

shave ice powdery ice shavings put in a paper cone and covered with sweet, flavored syrup

One morning, unable to stand his craving any longer, the magic shark disguised himself as a shave ice man and knocked on the door of the first little pig's house. "Little Pig, Little Pig, let me come in," he called. "I have plenty shave ice!"

The little pig peeked out of the window. He was hot and thirsty and the cool, colorful shave ice looked so tasty. He grabbed his money and started to open the door.

But, just in time, he saw a fin on the shave ice man's back and he knew it was really the magic shark. He quickly shut and locked the door.

The shark knocked harder and called, "Little Pig, Little Pig, let me come in."

"Oh no," cried the little pig. "Not by the hair on my chinny, chin, chin."

The magic shark was hot and hungry and the little pig's answer made him very mad. He yelled, "Little Pig, Little Pig, let me come in or I will huff and I will puff and I will blow your house down."

The little pig did not open his door. (After all he wasn't crazy, he knew what the magic shark wanted.)

So, the very mad magic shark huffed and the very mad magic shark puffed and the very mad magic shark blew down the first little pig's house.

The first little pig ran out of the back door and down the path to the house of the second little pig. The very mad magic shark went back to the ocean to cool off and make a new plan.

In a few days, the magic shark was hungry for little pigs again. This time he dressed up as a beachboy, wearing white pants, a coconut leaf hat, and a lei around his neck. He knocked on the door of the second little pig's house and called, "Little Pig, Little Pig, let's talk story and play ukes."

The little pigs grabbed their ukulele and nose flute and opened the door. The beachboy smiled and the little pigs saw rows and rows of long, sharp white teeth and just in time, they slammed the door.

106

"Little Pig, Little Pig, let me come in," called the hot and hungry magic shark anxiously.

"Oh no," cried the little pigs. (They knew that was no friendly beachboy out on the steps.) "Not by the hairs on our chinny, chin, chins."

This made the magic shark upset so he roared, "Then I will huff and I will puff and I will blow your house down." Just as he said he would, the very upset magic shark huffed and the very upset magic shark puffed and the very upset magic shark blew down the house of the second little pig.

The little pig and his brother jumped out of the window and ran down the path to the house of the third little pig.

mu'u mu'u (MOO oo MOO oo) a long, loose fitting woman's dress

lauhala (loo HAH lah) leaf of the hala or Pandanus tree; used in weaving hats, rugs, and baskets

Once more the magic shark, hot and still hungry, swam angrily down to his watery home to plot and scheme. After a few days his hunger pangs were so bad that the magic shark decided to try again.

This time he went pretending to be a lei seller. He knocked on the third little pig's door and called sweetly, "Little Pig, Little Pig, let me come in. I have leis to sell."

The three little pigs loved to wear leis and were happy to hear a sweet voice calling.

They looked out and saw the lei seller in her mu'u mu'u and lauhala hat, with flower leis on her arms. But then, they also saw a shark's tail sticking out from under the mu'u mu'u. They knew who that was so they rushed around locking the doors and windows.

"Little Pig, Little Pig, let me come in," called the magic shark, growing upset.

"Oh no," answered the little pigs. "Not by the hairs on our chinny, chin, chins."

"You will be sorry!" screamed the furious magic shark in his loudest voice. "I will huff and I will puff and I will blow your house down." No one answered and no one opened the door, so the furious magic shark huffed and the furious magic shark puffed and he huffed and he puffed and he blew . . . and nothing happened!

Again he huffed and he puffed and he huffed and he puffed and he blew and he blew and still nothing happened.

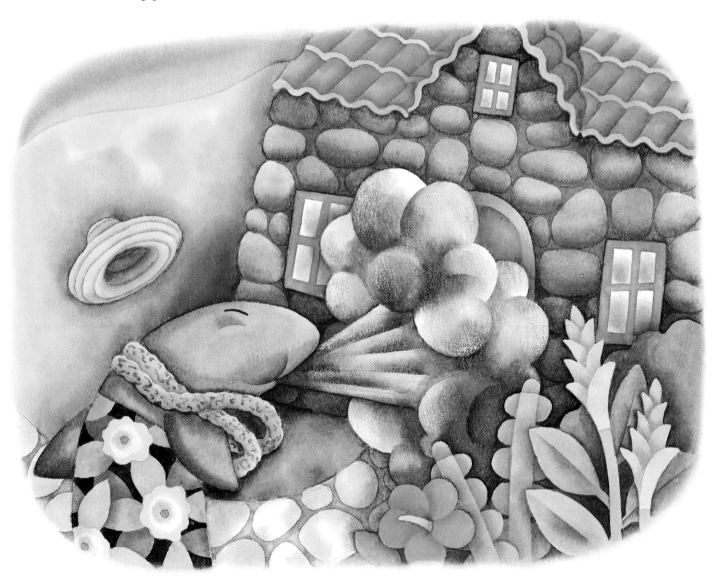

Once more the furious magic shark huffed and the furious magic shark puffed and the furious magic shark huffed and the furious magic shark puffed and the furious magic shark blew and blew and still . . . the lava rock house stood firm.

Now this made the magic shark extremely furious. So, gathering up all of his air, the extremely furious magic shark huffed and puffed and huffed and puffed and huffed and puffed

and blew
and blew
and blew
and blew
and blew
and blew
and blew

until . . . whoosh; ker-splat, he fell on the ground all out of air looking like a flat balloon!

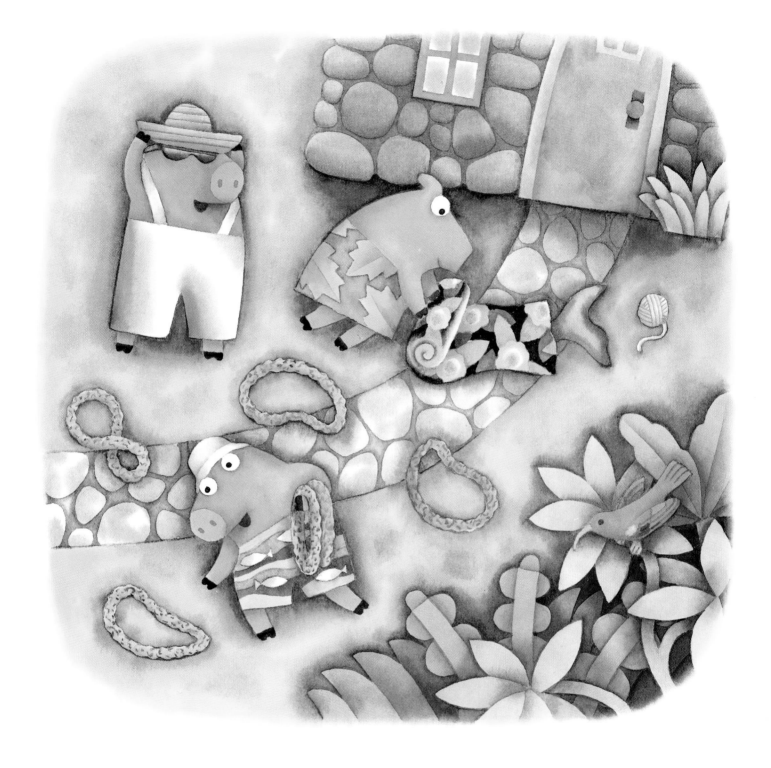

It was quiet and still and the three little pigs
cautiously peeked out of the house. Seeing the very flat
magic shark, they quickly ran outside, rolled him up
like a straw mat, and tied a string around him.

Then . . . taking him off to the dump they threw
him away.

When they returned to the seashore, the third little pig helped his brothers build sturdy rock houses and once they were finished, the three little pigs gave a large party. They invited all their friends and relatives as well as a shave ice man (without a fin) to serve

refreshments, a beachboy (without rows of sharp white teeth) to join the musicians, and a lei seller (without a shark's tail) to give out leis.

From then on the three little pigs lived safely and peacefully beside the sea.

Aloha, Little Pigs

Write a Paragraph

Dear Magic Shark

The shark didn't have much luck fooling the pigs. Can you think of a better disguise he could have used? Write a paragraph to give the shark advice on what to wear and how to act.

Act Out a Scene

Let Me Come In!

With a group of friends, act out your favorite scene from the story. You'll need one person to play each part and another to be the narrator. It might be fun to make props to help you tell the story.

Pigs

by
Charles Ghigna

Pigs are playful
Pigs are pink
Pigs are smarter
Than you think

Pigs are slippery
Pigs are stout
Pigs have noses
Called a snout

Pigs are pudgy
Pigs are plump
Pigs can run
But never jump

Pigs are loyal
Pigs are true
Pigs don't care for
Barbecue

115

Surprise, Surprise
A story by Kara Johnson

Mr. Pig has a surprise in store for him! Read what happens on his special day.

Surprise, Surprise

It was a sunny day. The birds were singing, the trees and shrubs in full bloom, but Whooper City was a state of confusion. The streets were packed with people bustling all around.

Mr. Reindeer, the Whooper City mail carrier, had a very important letter for Mr. Pig. He could hear the shower running inside Mr. Pig's house. "Mr. Pig, Mr. Pig!" he screamed at the top of his lungs. Mr. Reindeer had a party to go to, so he was finishing his job as fast as possible. Finally, Mr. Pig came out in a towel and got the morning's mail.

A moment later Mr. Pig came down specially dressed because it was his birthday. He sifted through the mail, hoping to find a birthday card, but all he could find was a notice for a meeting at Ms. Rabbit's house. It read:

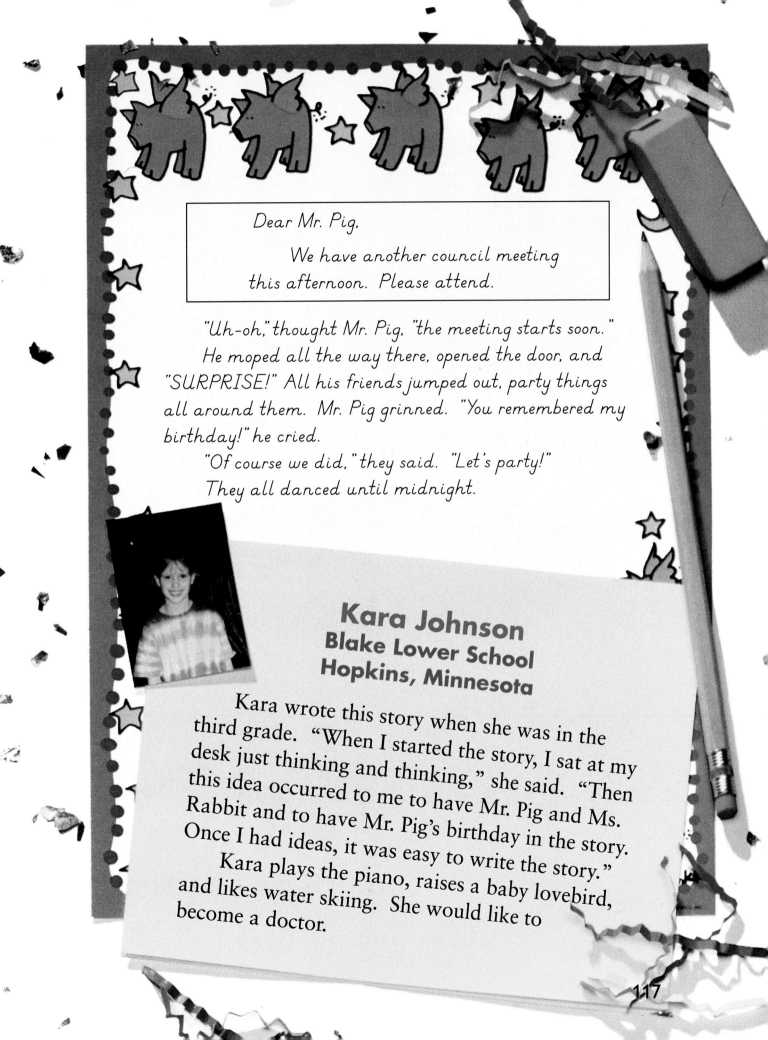

> Dear Mr. Pig,
>
> We have another council meeting this afternoon. Please attend.

"Uh-oh," thought Mr. Pig, "the meeting starts soon." He moped all the way there, opened the door, and "SURPRISE!" All his friends jumped out, party things all around them. Mr. Pig grinned. "You remembered my birthday!" he cried.

"Of course we did," they said. "Let's party!"

They all danced until midnight.

Kara Johnson
Blake Lower School
Hopkins, Minnesota

Kara wrote this story when she was in the third grade. "When I started the story, I sat at my desk just thinking and thinking," she said. "Then this idea occurred to me to have Mr. Pig and Ms. Rabbit and to have Mr. Pig's birthday in the story. Once I had ideas, it was easy to write the story."

Kara plays the piano, raises a baby lovebird, and likes water skiing. She would like to become a doctor.

The Wild Boar & the Fox

An Aesop's Fable retold by Dr. Albert Cullum

Characters: Boar, Fox

Staging: The story takes place in the middle of a forest. A large table or desk can represent a sturdy tree trunk.

Boar: Now that I have a moment, I think I will sharpen my teeth. Here is a nice sturdy tree that will help me. *(Rubs and rubs his tusks against the very hard tree trunk.)*

Fox: What in the world are you doing, Boar?

Boar: I'm sharpening my tusks.

Fox: That seems like a very silly thing to be doing.

Boar: Really! Why?

Fox: It's silly, for I don't see any danger about. I don't see a hunter and his dogs coming after you!

Boar: I don't see a hunter and his dogs coming after me, either.

Fox: Well, then, why all the nonsense about sharpening your tusks?

Boar: Fox, I don't think you understand. Wouldn't it be foolish of me to wait until the hunter and his dogs attacked before I sharpened my tusks? I think you are silly, not me!

Moral:
Think ahead and be prepared.

Some of the words in this book may have pronunciations or meanings you do not know. This glossary can help you by telling you how to pronounce those words and by telling you the meanings for the words as they are used in this book.

You can find out how to pronounce any glossary word by using the special spelling after the word and the key that runs across the bottom of the glossary pages.

The full pronunciation key on the next page shows how to pronounce each consonant and vowel in a special spelling. The pronunciation key at the bottom of the glossary pages is a shortened form of the full key.

Full Pronunciation Key

Consonant Sounds

b	**b**i**b**, ca**bb**age	kw	**ch**oir, **qu**ick	t	**t**igh**t**, stopp**ed**
ch	**ch**ur**ch**, sti**tch**	l	**l**id, need**l**e, ta**ll**	th	ba**th**, **th**in
d	**d**ee**d**, mail**ed**, pu**dd**le	m	a**m**, **m**an, du**mb**	*th*	ba**th**e, **th**is
		n	**n**o, sudd**en**	v	ca**v**e, val**v**e, **v**ine
f	**f**ast, **f**i**f**e, o**ff**, **ph**rase, rou**gh**	ng	thi**ng**, i**nk**	w	**w**ith, **w**olf
		p	**p**o**p**, ha**pp**y	y	**y**es, **y**olk, on**i**on
g	**g**a**g**, **g**et, fin**g**er	r	**r**oa**r**, **rh**yme	z	ro**s**e, si**z**e, **x**ylophone, **z**ebra
h	**h**at, **wh**o	s	mi**ss**, **s**auce, **sc**ene, **s**ee		
hw	**wh**ich, **wh**ere			zh	gara**g**e, plea**s**ure, vi**s**ion
j	**j**u**dg**e, **g**em	sh	di**sh**, **sh**ip, **s**ugar, ti**ss**ue		
k	**c**at, **k**i**ck**, s**ch**ool				

Vowel Sounds

ă	r**a**t, l**au**gh	ŏ	h**o**rrible, p**o**t	ŭ	c**u**t, fl**oo**d, r**ou**gh, s**o**me
ā	**a**pe, **ai**d, p**ay**	ō	g**o**, r**ow**, t**oe**, th**ough**		
â	**ai**r, c**a**re, w**ea**r			û	c**i**rcle, f**u**r, h**ea**rd, t**er**m, t**u**rn, **u**rge, w**or**d
ä	f**a**ther, k**oa**la, y**a**rd	ô	**a**ll, c**au**ght, f**o**r, p**aw**		
ĕ	p**e**t, pl**ea**sure, **a**ny	oi	b**oy**, n**oi**se, **oi**l	yōō	c**u**re
ē	b**e**, b**ee**, **ea**sy, p**ia**no	ou	c**ow**, **ou**t	yōō	**a**b**u**se, **u**se
ĭ	**i**f, p**i**t, b**u**sy	ōō	f**u**ll, t**oo**k, w**o**lf	ə	**a**bout, sil**e**nt, penc**i**l, lem**o**n, circ**u**s
ī	b**y**, p**ie**, h**igh**	ōō	b**oo**t, fr**ui**t, fl**ew**		
î	d**ear**, d**eer**, f**ie**rce, m**ere**				

Stress Marks

Primary Stress **'**: bi•ol•o•gy [bī **ŏl´** ə jē]
Secondary Stress ': bi•o•log•i•cal [bī´ ə **lŏj´** i kəl]

A

a•do•be (ə **dō´** bē) *noun* Brick that is made from clay and straw and dried in the sun: *Many houses in the southwestern United States are built with* **adobe**.

adobe

ADOBE
Adobe is a Spanish word. It goes back to the Arabic word *attoba* meaning "the brick."

an•xious•ly (**ăngk´** shəs lē´) *adverb* In a worried way: *The crowd watched* **anxiously** *as the firefighter carried the child down the ladder.*

C

cac•tus (**kăk´** təs) *noun* A plant with thick, often spiny, leafless stems that grows in hot, dry places.

cactus

crav•ing (**krā´** vĭng) *noun* A very strong desire for something: *As I passed the bakery, I suddenly had a* **craving** *for a piece of apple pie.*

D

des•ert (**dĕz´** ərt) *noun* A dry area of land that is usually sandy and without trees: *Very few plants grow in the* **desert** *because it hardly ever rains.*

DESERT
Desert comes from a Latin word meaning "to abandon, or leave behind." When a place was abandoned, it was called a *desert*.

dust storm (dŭst stôrm) *noun* Strong winds that carry clouds of sand and dust across an area: *During*

ă rat / ā pay / â care / ä father / ĕ pet / ē be / ĭ pit / ī pie / î fierce / ŏ pot / ō go / ô paw, for / oi oil /
o͞o took

Glossary 3

the **dust storm**, Dad had to stop the car because he couldn't see to drive.

F

fu•ri•ous (**fyŏŏr´** ē əs) *adjective* Full of anger: *Carlos was **furious** when he saw that the puppy had chewed his favorite shoes.*

G

grunt (grŭnt) *verb* To say or speak in a short, deep, harsh voice: *Grandpa sleepily **grunted** an answer to my question.*

P

pang (păng) *noun* A short but sharp feeling, as of pain: *Just before dinner, I began having little **pangs** of hunger.*

plot (plŏt) *verb* To plan secretly: *Dad will **plot** a way to sneak Mom's birthday present into the house without her seeing it.*

prowl (proul) *verb* To sneak about as if hunting or looking for something: *The stray dog was **prowling** the streets looking for food.*

S

scheme (skēm) *verb* To make up a plan for: *Our team will **scheme** to win the game.*

T

trem•ble (**trĕm´** bəl) *verb* **1.** To shake from fear or the cold: *I knew Aunt Shirley was afraid of something when I saw her hands **trembling**.* **2.** To shake: *The earthquake made our house **tremble**.*

tum•ble•weed (**tŭm´** bəl wēd´) *noun* A plant that breaks off from its roots when it dies and is blown about in the wind.

tumbleweed

ōō b**oo**t / ou **ou**t / ŭ c**u**t / û f**u**r / hw **wh**ich / th **th**in / *th* **th**is / zh vi**s**ion / ə **a**bout, sil**e**nt, penc**i**l, lem**o**n, circ**u**s

W

whirl•wind (**wûrl´** wĭnd´) *noun*
A current of air that spins rapidly
around: *The **whirlwind** picked up
the pile of leaves and spun them
around in circles.*

ă rat / ā pay / â care / ä father / ĕ pet / ē be / ĭ pit / ī pie / î fierce / ŏ pot / ō go / ô paw, for / oi oil /
o͞o took

Glossary 5

ACKNOWLEDGMENTS

For each of the selections listed below, grateful acknowledgment is made for permission to excerpt and/or reprint original or copyrighted material as follows:

Selections

Miss Nelson Is Missing! by Harry Allard, illustrated by James Marshall. Text copyright © 1977 by Harry Allard. Illustrations copyright © 1977 by James Marshall. Reprinted by permission of Houghton Mifflin Company. All rights reserved.

"My Hairy Neighbors," by Susan Lowell, from March 1994 *Ranger Rick* magazine. Copyright © 1994 by The National Wildlife Federation. Reprinted by permission.

"Pronunciation Key," from the *American Heritage Children's Dictionary.* Copyright © 1994 by Houghton Mifflin Company. Reprinted by permission. All rights reserved.

This Little Piggy, by Linda Granfield, from November 1992 *Owl* magazine. Copyright © 1992 by Linda Granfield. Reprinted by permission of the author and the Young Naturalist Foundation.

The Three Little Hawaiian Pigs and the Magic Shark, by Donivee Martin Laird. Copyright © 1981 by Donivee Martin Laird. Reprinted by permission of Barnaby Books, a Hawaii Partnership.

The Three Little Javelinas, by Susan Lowell, illustrated by Jim Harris. Text copyright © 1992 by Susan Lowell. Illustrations copyright © 1992 by Jim Harris. Reprinted by permission of Northland Publishing, Flagstaff, AZ.

The Three Little Wolves and the Big Bad Pig, by Eugene Trivizas, illustrated by Helen Oxenbury. Text copyright © 1993 by Eugene Trivizas. Illustrations copyright © 1993 by Helen Oxenbury. Reprinted by permission of Margaret K. McElderry Books, Simon & Schuster Children's Publishing Division. First published by Heinemann Young Books in Great Britain.

"What's Up, Pup?" by Lyle Prescott, from July 1994 *Ranger Rick* magazine. Copyright © 1994 by The National Wildlife Federation. Reprinted by permission.

"The Wild Boar & The Fox," from *Aesop's Fables: Plays For Young Children,* by Dr. Albert Cullum. Copyright © 1993 by Fearon Teacher Aids, an imprint of Modern Curriculum Press. Reprinted by permission of Simon & Schuster Elementary.

Poetry

"Pigs," by Charles Ghigna, from January 1993 *Ranger Rick* magazine. Copyright © 1993 by Charles Ghigna. Reprinted by permission of the author.

Additional Acknowledgments

Special thanks to the following teacher whose student's composition is included in the Be a Writer feature in this theme: David Burton, Blake Lower School, Hopkins, Minnesota.

CREDITS

Illustration 12–27 James Marshall 37–59 Helen Oxenbury 92–113 Don Stuart 115 Brian Lies 118–119 Loretta Lustig **Back cover inset** Don Stuart (m)

Assignment Photography Cover/Back cover Tony Scarpetta (background); Tracey Wheeler (cover inset) **Title page** Tony Scarpetta (background, insets) 6–7 Tony Scarpetta 8–9, 10–11 Glen Kremer 28 Tracey Wheeler 29 Tony Scarpetta 36 David Desroches 60 Tony Scarpetta 144 Banta Digital Group; Tracey Wheeler 116–117 Tony Scarpetta **Back cover insets** Glen Kremer (bm); Banta Digital Group (bl)

Photography 28 Courtesy of Harry Allard (tl); Courtesy of Houghton Mifflin Co. (tr) 36 Courtesy of Helen Oxenbury; Courtesy of Eugene Trivizas and Reed Children's Books (t); © Otto Rogge/The Stock Market (t, b) 61 Ranger Rick Magazine; Art Wolfe 62 Art Wolfe (tr, bl) 63 Art Wolfe (tr, b); Ranger Rick Magazine (b) 64 © Andrew Sacks/© Tony Stone Images/Chicago, Inc. 65 © David Falconer/DRK Photo (t); John Colwell/ Grant Heilman Photography (b) 66 The Bettmann Archive (t); © Andrew Sacks/Tony Stone Images/Chicago Inc. (b) 67 © Stephen J. Krasemann/DRK Photo (t); © Phil Dotson/Photo Researchers (t); Alain Compost/Bruce Coleman, Inc. (t); Robert Barclay/Grant Heilman Photography (b) 68–69 Mark Muench/© Tony Stone Images/Chicago Inc. 68 Ross Humphreys/Courtesy of Susan Lowell (t); Courtesy of Jim Harris (b) 88 Rene Lynn/Photo Researchers 89 Thomas A. Wiewand (tr) 90–91 Thomas A. Wiewand 92 Courtesy of Donivee M. Laird (tl); Courtesy of Don Stuart (br) 117 Courtesy of Kara Johnson **Glossary 3** The Image Bank (tl); Joe Szkoozinski/The Image Bank (tr) **Glossary 4** Patti Murray/Animals Animals (br)